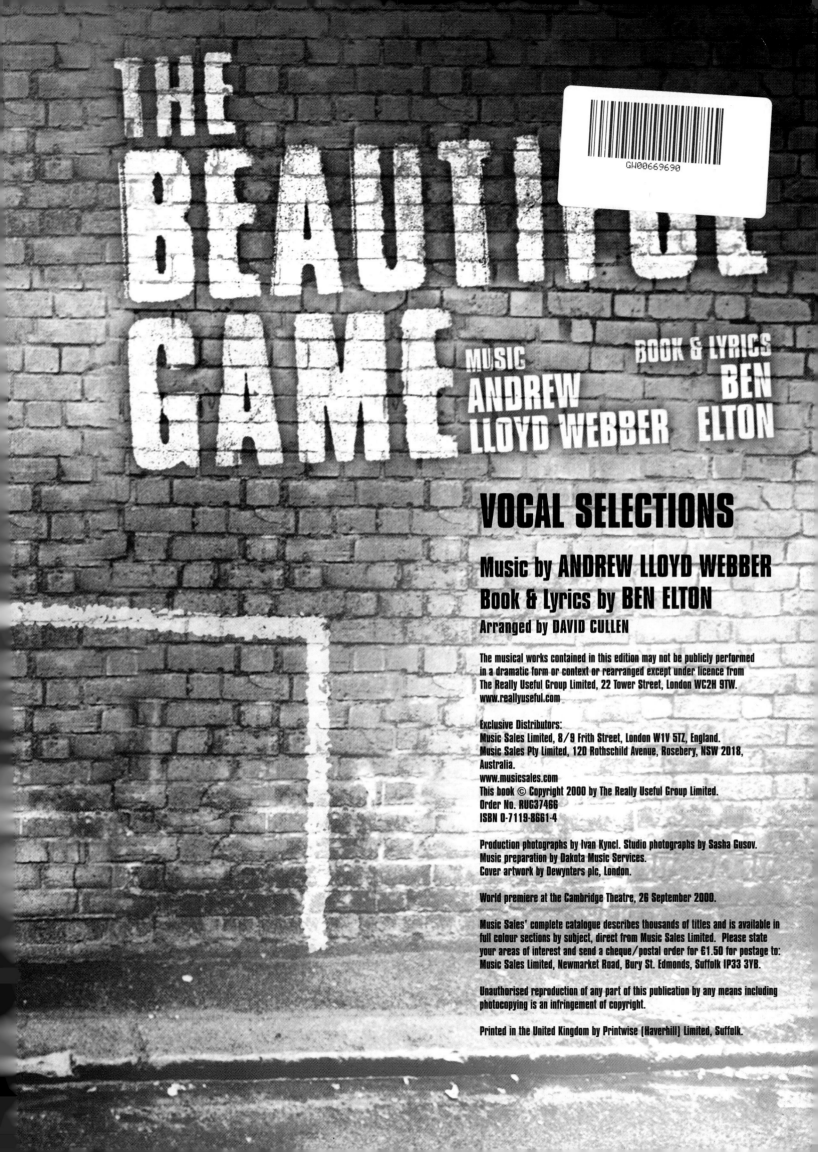

THE BEAUTIFUL GAME

MUSIC ANDREW LLOYD WEBBER

BOOK & LYRICS BEN ELTON

VOCAL SELECTIONS

Music by ANDREW LLOYD WEBBER

Book & Lyrics by BEN ELTON

Arranged by DAVID CULLEN

Exclusive Distributors:
Music Sales Limited, 8/9 Frith Street, London W1V 5TZ, England.
Music Sales Pty Limited, 120 Rothschild Avenue, Rosebery, NSW 2018, Australia.
www.musicsales.com
This book © Copyright 2000 by The Really Useful Group Limited.
Order No. RUG37466
ISBN 0-7119-8661-4

Production photographs by Ivan Kyncl. Studio photographs by Sasha Gusov.
Music preparation by Dakota Music Services.
Cover artwork by Dewynters plc, London.

World premiere at the Cambridge Theatre, 26 September 2000.

Music Sales' complete catalogue describes thousands of titles and is available in full colour sections by subject, direct from Music Sales Limited. Please state your areas of interest and send a cheque/postal order for £1.50 for postage to:
Music Sales Limited, Newmarket Road, Bury St. Edmonds, Suffolk IP33 3YB.

Printed in the United Kingdom by Printwise (Haverhill) Limited, Suffolk.

THE BEAUTIFUL GAME

MUSIC BY ANDREW LLOYD WEBBER
LYRICS BY BEN ELTON

Slow Heavy Rock

Meas - ure your life in foot - ball seas - ons. Feel the pass - ion and feel the heat.

Foot - ball is the on - ly reas - on. God al - migh - ty gave us feet.

GOAL! Buy the ref a flip-ping guide dog.

D'you call that a bleed-ing pass? Kick it out mate! What a ball hog!

Do - zy plonk - er, shift your arse! TWO NIL!

You stu - pid plonk - er, we're going to con - quer. Come and have a go. Have some of that. You

a mag-i-cal game. Thank God for foot - ball._____

Girls — They're our__ lads and we sup-port 'em, come on then__ stick one in this time. It

is-n't a re-li-gion it's more im-por-tant, sa-cred,__ ho-ly and di-vine

THREE   NIL!   Nice one Un-i-ted.   We're all de-light - ed.

9

soc - cer the game. Score_____ a thou - sand more for the Boys in Green,

the E - mer - ald team. Play - ing for Ire - land.

Play - ing for Ire - land._____

ALL THE LOVE I HAVE

MUSIC BY ANDREW LLOYD WEBBER
LYRICS BY BEN ELTON

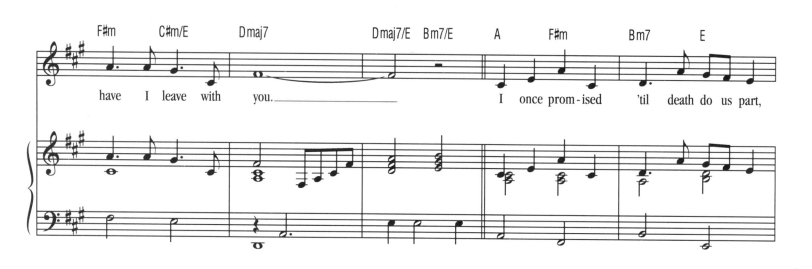

such a stu-pid sa-cri-fice.____ Don't you un-der-stand____ that this won't

end 'til we let it. When I'm gone you know I won't be back.

Mine's a path that has no turn-ing. Please be-lieve me what I said was

true, that all the love I have I leave with you.

rall.

John

DON'T LIKE YOU

MUSIC BY ANDREW LLOYD WEBBER
LYRICS BY BEN ELTON

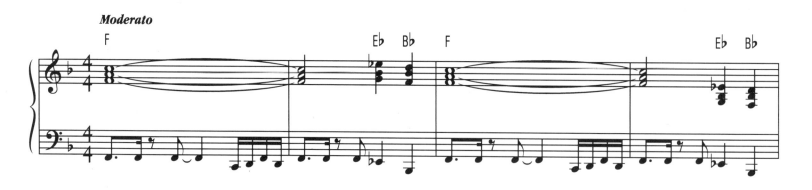

Mary

Don't like you. Don't like you. I don't think I

like you. You're bad, you're sad, and

17

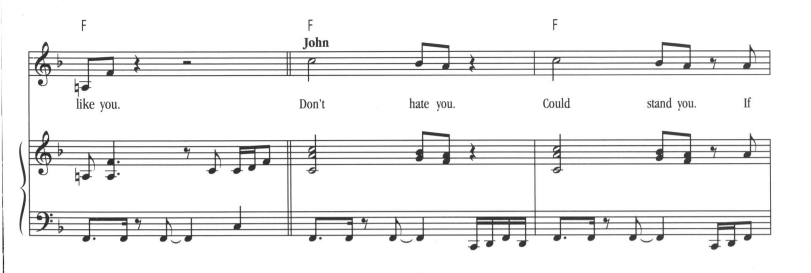

like you. Don't hate you. Could stand you. If

pushed_____ could tol - er - ate you. I'm sure that you'll mat -

ure, I have known_____ more stu - pid boys.

22

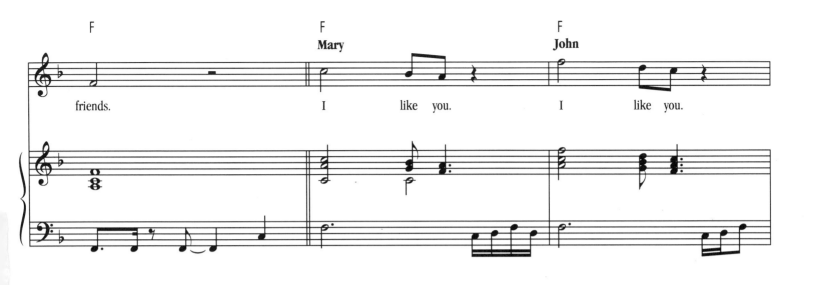

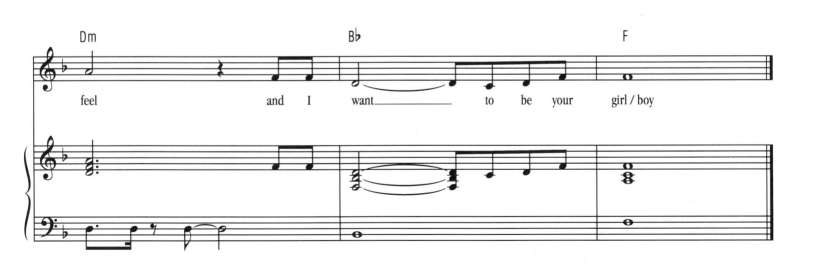

THE FIRST TIME

MUSIC BY ANDREW LLOYD WEBBER
LYRICS BY BEN ELTON

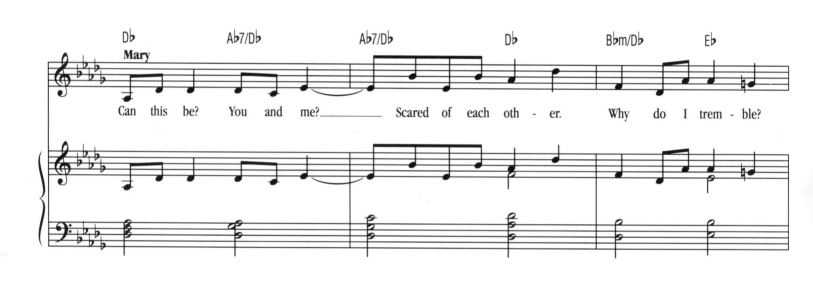

Mary

Can this be? You and me?_____ Scared of each oth - er. Why do I trem - ble?

The first time's not a crime so let's not wait. It's our fate. Make me your lov - er,____

si - tion does a girl pre - fer? I fear pre - ma - ture e - jac - u -

la - tion. 'Cos my God I don't half fan - cy her.

Mary
If I seem less than keen, _____ it's not e - va - sion. I'm scared I'll be a

John
piece of wood, not much good. Close my eyes, try to rise _____ to the oc - ca - sion. _____

GOD'S OWN COUNTRY

MUSIC BY ANDREW LLOYD WEBBER
LYRICS BY BEN ELTON

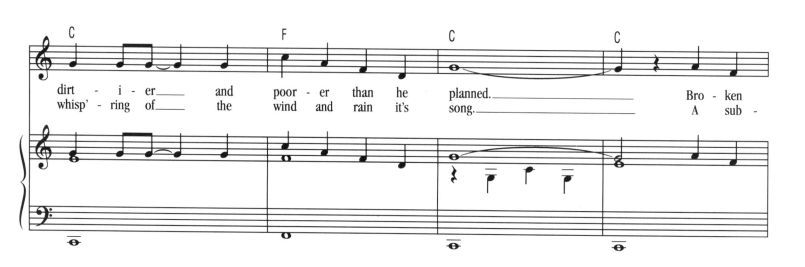

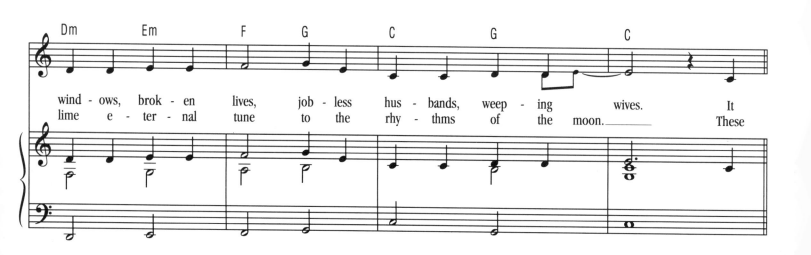

may not look like God's own coun - try. But God is
an - cient chords were formed in the be - gin - ning. And they

love and I know he loves this land._____ Though it's
sing to me____ "My coun - try right or wrong",_____ These are

rag - ged and it's worn, it's the place where I was born. The
songs we al - ways sang, no - one knows when where they be - gan.

beau - ty lies with - in____ in God's own coun - try. It sleeps be -
This fair land is God's own coun - try. And it's

IF THIS IS WHAT WE'RE FIGHTING FOR

MUSIC BY ANDREW LLOYD WEBBER
LYRICS BY BEN ELTON

LET US LOVE IN PEACE

MUSIC BY ANDREW LLOYD WEBBER
LYRICS BY BEN ELTON

TO HAVE AND TO HOLD

MUSIC BY ANDREW LLOYD WEBBER
LYRICS BY BEN ELTON

OUR KIND OF LOVE

MUSIC BY ANDREW LLOYD WEBBER
LYRICS BY BEN ELTON

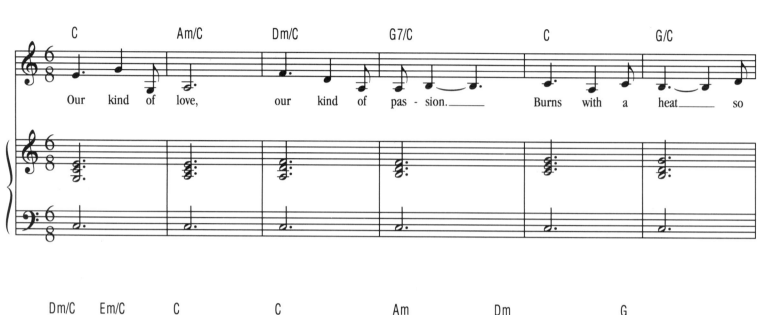

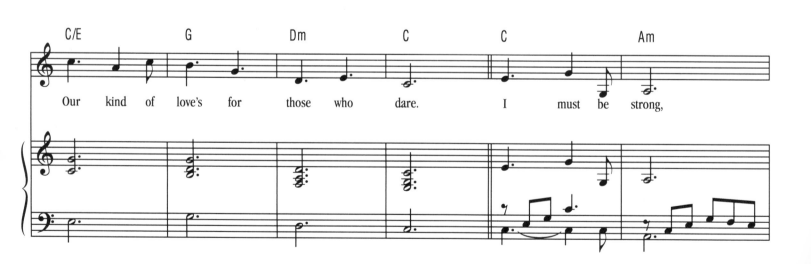